The Geat

The story of Beowulf and Grendel

Retold by John Harris

Illustrated by Tom Morgan-Jones

notreallybooks

For
Gil Barrow
Penny Horsman
Sally Wrigley
and
Andrea Harris

without whom this version of the story
would not have evolved

Before we begin.....

I like to think of this as the original horror story. It's certainly one of the oldest stories in the English language. It was first written down about fifteen hundred years ago, but it`s much older than that because in those days stories were told for a long time before anyone bothered to write them down. This story is probably about two thousand years old.

What I'd like you to think about when you're reading this is how different the world was two thousand years ago from what it`s like now. There were none of the things we take for granted today: planes, cars, trains, motorbikes, TVs, radios, computers, phones. There was no electricity. The world then was so much quieter than our world that it was almost silent in comparison. The loudest sound you would hear in those days was that of a thunderstorm and - if you were unfortunate enough - the sound of battle.

It was also a much darker world. The only light they had was daylight or moonlight, firelight and candle light. No electric lights, no torches, no floodlights. There were a lot more trees and forests in those days - they didn`t cut them down as thoughtlessly as we have done - and if you found yourself in one of those forests at night, with only the moon to guide you, it could be very frightening. That's why we have so many old stories about dark, scary woods.

That`s what the world was like all those years ago.

That's the world in which this story takes place.

Chapter One

Hrothgar was the king of the Danes. He was the great-grandson of Scyld Scefing, who had also been king, and although no-one could ever match Scyld Scefing for courage and heroic deeds, Hrothgar had come close. He was a good king: wise, brave, clever and kind; he was loved by his people. He also liked a good time as much as anyone else did.

In those days it was the job of a king to protect his people: from other kingdoms who might want to invade his country; from marauding robbers and cut-throat pirates; even from wild, savage beasts that roamed the dark woods waiting to tear apart anyone unfortunate enough to wander too far from home.

And Hrothgar had done all that. When he first became king he set about creating the finest army in the world. A band of soldiers who were as brave and cool headed as they were well trained and disciplined. They were slick, fast, daring and ruthless. They fought fairly but they rarely took prisoners - at the end of one of their battles there were rarely any prisoners to take.

Their reputation had spread so far that for many years they had nothing much to do. No-one threatened the Danes. On the contrary - other kings regularly sent gifts to Hrothgar to pay homage to him and avoid any trouble. The last thing they wanted was for Hrothgar to send his soldiers.

After many years as king, Hrothgar was beginning to feel a little old. In those days people didn't live much past their sixties and Hrothgar was in his fifties, and beginning to wonder how much time he had left in this world. He knew that some day he would die, as all men must, but he hoped he would be remembered for a long time after his death. He began to wonder about leaving something behind which would help his people remember him even after he was long gone.

He thought about composing a song, but then discovered that forging a good tune wasn`t any easier than forging metal. He tried writing his life story as a poem, but when he read it aloud to Wealtheow, his wife, he couldn't help but notice the glazed look in her eyes, so he gave up on the poetry.

But at supper one night he had a flash of inspiration: he was sitting at the high table in the hall of his castle, watching his family, friends, soldiers and servants eating, drinking and laughing. Later there would be music and dancing. When Hrothgar thought of the fuss involved in clearing the tables and pushing them back to make room to dance he suddenly realised what they needed was a new hall with enough space for all their needs. If he built such a hall everyone would remember him every time they had a party - which was quite often.

The Danes loved parties. Their parties were the kind that everyone was invited to and to which everyone was truly welcome. They sometimes lasted for days and nights at a time - everyone knew when a party would begin but no-one was sure when it would end. As well as eating and drinking, singing and dancing, there would be poets and storytellers, musicians, jugglers and jesters. Other guests would tell stories and sing songs of their own, propose toasts and sometimes even make speeches. They would be cheered, and sometimes jeered, but it was always good hearted because everyone was enjoying themselves.

Hrothgar's castle was on the top of a hill, overlooking cliffs which in turn overlooked the sea. But behind the castle, at the bottom of the hill, was a huge dark forest that stretched for miles. Hrothgar ordered a clearing to be made at the bottom of the hill at the edge of the forest, and the timber from the trees was to be used to build the hall in the clearing.

It took a while to build, but when it was finished everyone agreed it was the most wonderful hall they could ever have dreamed of. It was so big that over a hundred people could be sitting at tables and there would still be room for the dancing. The front door was made of solid oak with iron handles and hinges. The floor and walls were made of different kinds of wood, carefully crafted together to bring out the different hues and colours of the wood in intricate patterns. Huge oak joists and rafters held the whole thing together, and all over the building - inside and out - were

examples of the finest, most detailed and intricate craftsmanship.

Hrothgar gave the hall its own special name: Heorot. When it was finished a party was arranged to which everyone was invited - not just important people like royalty and nobility from every land and tribe the Danes knew, but all the ordinary people who lived anywhere within reach of the hall. Rich or poor, they were all invited and they were all welcome, and it seemed as if they all turned up. Some sailed boats along the coast from further upland, while others journeyed for several days across the bleak moors on the far side of the forest. The wind had howled around them as if trying to blow them off course, and the rain and sleet had hit their faces like slaps from ice cold fingers, but the warmth and welcome they found at the end of their journey made it all worthwhile. The place was heaving for three days and three nights and no-one could remember such a good party for many, many years.

But all good things must come to an end, and when Hrothgar finally announced that he`d had enough and needed to get to bed everyone knew that it was time to go home. Those who lived nearby thanked the king for his hospitality and set off for home, while those who lived in, or were staying at, the castle began to stagger back up the hill to their beds. Hrothgar thanked the servants for all their hard work and told them to go to bed and leave the clearing up until the next day, for which they were very grateful. Then he

asked six of his soldiers to stay behind until the morning just to keep an eye on the hall, which of course they were happy to do.

So, in a short space of time the hall which had been a bustling and noisy hive of activity fell into a peaceful, calm silence.

If truth be known, the soldiers who were asked to stay behind were as tired as anyone else. They'd been at the party, had as much as anyone else to eat and drink, and needed to sleep as much as anyone else. They didn't see any need to stay awake because if anything happened they'd hear and wake up. And anyway, what could happen?
They found blankets and furs in chests at the back of the hall, laid them down in the middle of the floor close to each other for warmth, and in no time at all fell fast asleep.

Which was a mistake.

It was a mistake because over the last few nights the sound of the party had travelled through the still and silent air of the thick, dark forest and then beyond the forest to the dark, damp, slimy swamp on the far side.

At the far edge of the swamp was a small hill, and just at the point where the brown slimy mud lapped against the lower part of the hill a hole had been burrowed in the ground. It could easily have been mistaken for a foxhole, but it was larger, the entrance to a tunnel which wound underground, deep into and under the hill for quite some way before reaching a dank, damp lair in which there was a nest.

The nest was made of bones: bear bones, deer bones, wolf, cow, dog and sheep bones. And human bones. It was lined with the skins and furs of the animals whose bones had been used to build it. And in this nest there slept a creature every single person who had been at the party had heard of, but not one of them believed really existed.

And that was another mistake, because it did.

This creature was Grendel. Huge and hideous, disfigured and twisted, he was partly wild man, partly wolf, partly troll, partly who knows what. As strong as a dozen men and as wild as the wind, he had lived in that lair for as long as he could remember, and that was a long time.

His skin was thick and leathery. It was encrusted with mud and slime from the swamp mixed with the blood and remains of his victims. It was said that he was ancient, perhaps hundreds of years old, and could sleep for as long as some men lived.

This, of course, was why the people at the party, who had heard all the stories about Grendel since their childhood, didn`t actually believe them: hardly anyone at the party had even been born the last time Grendel had crept out of the swamp and through the forest.

But all that was about to change.

He stretched and yawned and started to wake up, and as he did so he gradually realised that what had woken him up was the sound of singing, dancing and laughter. The sound of human beings at their noisiest. He hated human beings, had

hated them since he was young. At the back of his mind was a distant memory of him wanting to be friends with some children when he too was very young. He had watched them playing for a while from the shelter of some trees and then summoned the courage to approach them. As he lumbered out from the trees they screamed and ran away from him. He stood where he was for a moment, unsure as to what to do, and then it seemed as if every person in the village was running towards him, screaming and shouting.

His animal instincts told him they were behaving that way because they were afraid, but he couldn't understand why they were afraid, he only wanted to play. He stood where he was for a moment but then they began to throw stones and rocks and then menfolk appeared and began to fire arrows and throw spears at him. Still he stood, wondering what to do, but when he saw another man running towards him holding fire on a branch knew it was time to leave. The spears and arrows had hurt his feelings more than his body but he'd seen fire at the edge of the forest once and knew what it could do.

By the time he returned to the safety of the trees he knew the depths of their hatred, and his sense of rejection grew into contempt for those who were too stupid to realise he'd meant them no harm. Over the years the contempt had grown to a hatred for them that was as strong as their fear of him.

Now he hated humans with all his heart, and he was furious to think that his sleep had been disturbed by the sound of humans enjoying themselves. How dare they? He would teach them not to do that again for a long time! He climbed out of his nest, slithered along the tunnel to the entrance and then glided through the warm, slimy mud of the swamp.

He was amphibious. He could breathe under water and in the air but his breathing had a hoarse, wheezy rattle to it, which alerted all the creatures of the forest once he reached dry land. None of them had ever seen this thing before but they knew instinctively to get away. Not all of them were quick enough: Grendel lashed out and crushed them in his hands, stuffing skin, bones, blood, flesh, meat, feathers into his mouth all at once.

Once he'd had something to eat he realised just how hungry he really was. He crept and crawled and crunched his way through the forest, looking for something more substantial until he suddenly found himself in a clearing.

A clearing in what he regarded as his forest. A clearing which hadn`t been here the last time he was here. This clearing had obviously been made by human beings, and they had put one of their horrible wood-buildings into the clearing. Then he realised this was where the noise had come from, all the noise that had woken him up. Well, that wouldn`t happen again...

He moved out from the trees and across the clearing. Straightening himself up as much as he could, he raised one arm and with the strength of twelve men slammed his arm onto the solid oak door.

The door flew in off its hinges and split into pieces as it hit the floor. The sleeping soldiers woke up instantly. They were well trained, brave and well disciplined. In one swift movement they leapt to their feet, drew their swords and ran towards the door. The last thing they ever saw was the most terrifying thing they`d ever seen. They ran towards it with their swords held in front of them but the monster simply gathered them up, three in each arm, and lifted them off the floor so that their feet were kicking helplessly in the air.

A moment later they each knew how they were going to die: the monster began to crush them with his arms. First they felt an incredible pain shoot through them from top to bottom as the creature fractured their spines. Unable to move, but still able to feel, they were helpless as the creature squeezed them so tightly that their hearts, livers, kidneys and intestines started to burst inside them under the pressure and the blood seeped from their mouths, noses and even their ears. Then, when the pressure was too much, their eyeballs burst out of their sockets, bounced off the walls and rolled across the floor.

Grendel didn`t like the heads, so he twisted them off and dropped them to the ground. He ate one of the bodies straight away and then left the hall carrying the other five across his shoulders. They would fit nicely in his lair and stop him feeling hungry during the day.

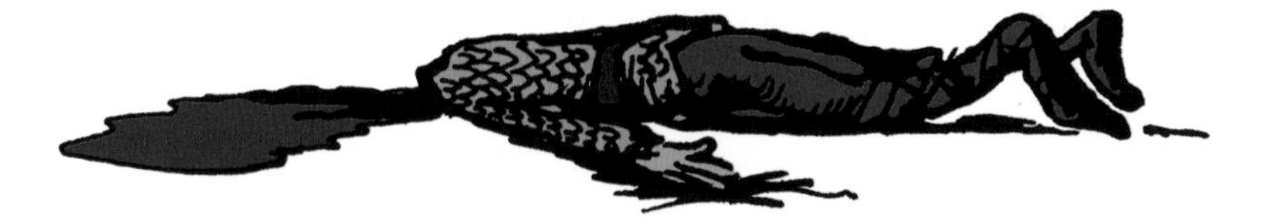

Chapter Two

When Hrothgar woke the next morning he turned to Wealtheow and said, "Ugh! I`m glad I`m awake! I was having the most awful nightmare!"

"I`m not surprised," she said rather drily, "do you have any idea how much you knocked back at that party? No wonder you had nightmares."

"It was more than a horrible dream, it was a sign of something. A warning."

"What kind of a warning?"

"I dreamed that the inside of Heorot had been painted red. I don't know why. I just saw the inside of the hall and it was empty, and the walls were red. That must mean something."

"Yes,' she said, "it means you shouldn't eat cheese before you go to bed because it gives you indigestion and that gives you bad dreams."

"I`m serious - I know in my bones that it was a sign of some kind. I`m worried."

"Well if you`re really worried have Wulfgar send a couple of boys down to see that everything`s all right."

Wulfgar, Hrothgar's chamberlain, sent two kitchen boys down with a basket of breakfast things for the soldiers and instructions to come straight back if anything had happened. They laughed as they carried the basket between them down the path. What could have happened? He'd told them the king had had a dream but so what? Everyone has strange dreams from time to time, perhaps if you're getting on a bit you start to take them seriously. Even though they loved the old king they laughed at the thoughts of him worrying about what his dreams might mean.

They laughed until they got to the bottom of the hill, entered the clearing and saw the front door. Or rather, the lack of a front door. All that remained was the door frame leading into the darkness of the hall. They knew something was very, very wrong.

If there`d just been one of them he would have turned and run back to the castle there and then. But there were two of them, and neither wanted to admit to the other how scared he was. So without saying a word they quietly placed the basket on the ground, walked slowly towards the door frame and, after hesitating for a moment, crossed the threshold into the darkness of the silent hall.

It took a moment or two for their eyes to adjust to the darkness so at first they couldn`t see what had happened. It was only when one of them stood on something squelchy and lifted his boot to see that he`d stood on an eye that they realised just how bad things were.

By then they could see that the king`s dream had come true: the hall had been not so much painted as redecorated in red. There was blood all over the floor and on the walls and some of it had even splashed up on to the ceiling. By then their eyes had adjusted to the darkness enough for them to

be able to count the various parts scattered around the hall. Twelve eyes. Six heads. And no bodies.

They had the presence of mind not to scream in case whatever had done this was still within earshot, but they turned and ran as quickly as they could back out into the fresh air of the clearing. One of them stumbled and threw up all over the ground. The other waited anxiously, keeping an eye out all around him, and as soon as the other one had stopped vomiting they ran back up the hill to the castle and went straight to the king.

Hrothgar was horrified. It wasn't just that the dream had been so accurate. It almost seemed as if whoever had done this had entered his sleeping thoughts, taunting him with his helplessness to prevent it.

By the time he had gathered his Thanes, his closest advisers, his mood had turned to one of furious, fuming, blood-spitting rage. The thanes, brave soldiers and lords themselves, sat around the table in silence as the king stamped up and down the room, kicking and thumping the walls and tables and threatening to do far worse to whoever had done this.

"When I find out who ordered this to be done I'll hang him upside down and stick him like a pig!" The thanes slammed their fists on the table in agreement. "I'll flatten their entire country. Every little thing and every wretched person in it." All but one of them thumped the table. One man sat quietly and thoughtfully watching the others and gradually they noticed and turned to look at him.

"What`s the matter with you, Unferth?" he asked.

There was an uncomfortable silence. Unferth took a deep breath. "With the greatest of respect, your Royal Highness," he began, "I think you`re making a mistake."

"A mistake?!!!!" the king thundered. "What mistake? You think I can`t find out who did this? You doubt I can make them suffer for it? You think I should just let them get away with -"

"No, no, no, no, no!" Unferth held up his hands. "I don`t mean that."

"Then what do you mean?"

"Well," he cleared his throat, "you`re assuming that what was done in the hall last night was done by soldiers from another kingdom."

"Well they certainly didn't do it to themselves," Wulfgar pointed out. He was irritated, but then he'd never liked Unferth.

"Obviously they didn't do it themselves," Unferth replied as politely as he could without seeming to be sarcastic. "But I don't think anyone else did it either." He paused for a second and then emphasised, "I mean no - one."

"What on earth are you talking about?" Wulfgar asked.

"Well look at it this way," said Unferth. "We have the best soldiers. The finest, bravest, strongest and swiftest of any in the world."

"That's what we thought," Hrothgar said.

"So how could any other army do to our soldiers what was done last night? It doesn't make sense. Which other king has men who would dare to even think about doing what was done last night, let alone get away with it?" He paused while the idea was considered.

"Go on," Hrothgar said more thoughtfully.

"Another point to consider," Unferth continued, "is that the king and queen of every land in the northern half of the world was at the party in Heorot last night." He paused again. "They slept here in this castle and are still here now," he waved his arm to take in the whole castle. "Most of them are our friends, and those we don't quite trust are too frightened of us to do anything to arouse our wrath. This could not have been the work of anyone else`s soldiers," he concluded.

His argument had been persuasive and they were beginning to think he might be right. But that left one question. "Well if soldiers didn`t do this," one of the others asked, "who did?"

Unferth looked around the table. "I`d have thought that was obvious," he said. "This has to have been the work of Grendel - "

The cries of disbelief were almost drowned out by the laughter and ridicule. "Oh come on, Unferth!"

"You can`t believe that!"

"Grendel`s just a story you tell to naughty children!"

"There's no such creature."

"Really?" Unferth stood up and they all fell silent. He looked at each of them in turn. "How do we know? We all heard the stories when we were children. We all know what happens to stories that are passed down through the years: they change, they grow and the monsters in them get bigger and more fierce. But what if just some of the stories we heard when we were young turn out to be at least partly true? The stories say Grendel can sleep for as long as most of us have been alive. What if that turns out to be true? What if he`s been asleep until now, and now he's woken up?"

"I've got an idea," one of the others spoke up. "I was told Grendel's a creature of habit and he follows the same route every night. Perhaps we should tie you to a tree in the forest and leave you overnight. If you're not there in the morning we'll assume it was Grendel!" The others laughed at this, and even Hrothgar forced a smile.

Unferth was undeterred. He stood with his arms folded until, once again, they fell silent. "Last night I dreamed that everyone in this room was standing at the edge of a deep hole somewhere in a forest. As we stood looking down, trying to fathom how deep it was, one of us fell in and was never seen again. I've never had a dream like that before in my life, and I don't understand why I should suddenly dream like that last night. But I believe that the events of last night are connected in some way, and we have seen the work of Grendel." In the silence that followed Unferth quietly sat down again.

After a pause Hrothgar took a deep breath. "Well, the tales do tell of a creature of habit, so if it was Grendel who came to the hall last night he`ll more than likely be back there tonight. And as your king it`s my duty to be there to fight him myself." He looked around the table at each of them in turn as he continued, "None of you is obliged to go with me, but if you`d like to, I`d be glad of the company." That was the kind of invitation no-one could refuse, and everyone knew it. One by one they volunteered to go with Hrothgar, even though they knew they were probably volunteering for death.

For the rest of the day preparations were made for that night. The hall was cleaned up and washed down. The door was repaired and re-hung. Knives, swords and daggers were sharpened and the king and his thanes had their chainmail dipped in whale blubber to prevent the monster being able to get a firm grip of them if all else failed.

After supper that night the thirteen of them marched in silence down the hill from the castle and took up positions in the hall.

They sat dotted around in pairs or threes, some playing chess or cards, some chatting quietly, and they waited.

And they waited.

And gradually, as they waited, the hall fell into a deathly silence.

It`s said by some that the darkest hour of the night is just before the dawn. And in that darkest hour, when they had waited in silence for so long, some of them began to think that whatever had attacked the hall the night before wasn`t coming back, at least not that night. They began to think they might live to see the morning after all. Their spirits began to rise again as they sensed the dawn approaching.

But then some of them became aware of a strange sound off in the distance. A wheezy, rattling kind of sound that could hardly be heard at first because it was so far away. Gradually it became clearer and louder as it got closer and eventually they could all hear it. They listened in horror as it came closer, so close that they all knew that whatever it was was on the other side of the door.

And on the other side of the door Grendel stood and stared. Gradually he realised that the door he'd smashed down the night before was there again. He couldn't understand why, but his instincts told him this meant there was something to eat on the other side. Again he raised his fist and slammed it against the oak and again the door flew in off its hinges and Grendel followed it into the hall.

But this time there were loud, piercing screams as he crossed the threshold. A dozen screaming soldiers ran towards him and stuck their swords into him. But his skin was so ancient and leathery that the swords were no worse than pins and the soldiers were like irritating wasps buzzing around him. He swatted at the soldiers with such strength and speed that their heads were knocked clean off their shoulders and their bodies flew through the air, only to break against the walls and lie silent and still.

It was all over within two minutes. The last thane to charge towards Grendel was grabbed in both hands and held aloft. His body was twisted and pulled apart and one half was stuffed greedily into the creature's mouth. It was at this point that Hrothgar, who had been further back, did the one and only cowardly thing he ever did in his life: he turned and ran out of the back door and up the hill as quickly as he could towards his castle.

But he didn't quite make it. He was so overcome with the horror of what he'd seen that he felt faint and dizzy and fell onto the path unconscious.

After dawn a couple of guards were sent down from the castle to check on the hall and of course they found their king, still unconscious, on the path. They scooped him up and carried him back to the castle and he was gently, carefully put to bed so that when he woke up later that morning he thought, for a moment, he'd had another horrible dream. But as he came to his senses and woke up fully he realised that it was real.

From that morning things were different. Hrothgar was still the king of the Danes, but it was fear that ruled the land. Word of what had happened spread through the land like wild fire. Many of those who lived within reach of the forest or the swamp packed their belongings and moved elsewhere. Those who couldn't think of anywhere else to go spent their days scurrying about like frightened rabbits. When it started to get dark in the afternoons they would barricade themselves into their homes as best they could and at night they would sleep as hidden away from the monster as they could manage.

From that morning onwards Hrothgar was a broken man. He never talked to anyone about how he felt, but those closest to him sensed that he felt responsible for what had happened. It had been he who had allowed himself to think he'd been a great king, he who'd decided to celebrate his great reign by building Heorot. In doing so it had been he who had awoken the monster and brought on his people the one terrible enemy he couldn't protect them from. He was responsible for all this. He had failed his people, and that broke his heart.

The only thing he could do was to send poets, singers and storytellers to every other country in the world to tell the tales surrounding Grendel and to offer a huge reward to anyone who could kill the monster. And at first there were plenty of volunteers. Brave, perhaps foolhardy, young men who made the mistake of assuming that storytellers always exaggerate. The truth, they were sure, couldn't be as bad as they said it was.

They would make the journey to Hrothgar's castle, sometimes alone, sometimes in groups, always over confident. After a good supper and a warning from the king about what to expect they'd march down the path from the castle to Heorot and that would be the last anyone would ever see of them.

Gradually word spread that these brave young men never came home, and gradually people understood that the stories were true and that nothing and no-one could defeat such a monster.

The hall fell into disuse and disrepair. Instead of cheering and dancing, laughter and music, it became home to bats and rats, mice and spiders. Owls nested in the rafters and would fly out at night through the battered open doorway or the holes in the roof, and while they were out at night looking for their food Grendel would be in the forest looking for his. Every night he would take the same route through the trees and arrive, just before dawn, at the clearing. Every night he'd lurch across the threshold into the dark, decaying hall. Gradually the hall came to smell as deadly as Grendel's breath.

Chapter Three

For twelve long years no human dared go into the hall. For twelve long years Grendel roamed the forest at night, slithering back through the swamp to his lair as the dawn broke. And gradually, over those long years, Hrothgar became a frail and heartbroken old man. There was nothing he could do to protect his people from the creature. All he could do was send soldiers out in the darkening afternoon to warn people of the dangers of being out any later. Sometimes these soldiers never returned to the castle, and nothing would be known for certain until, some time later, another soldier would come across a sword or a helmet in the forest or near the swamp. Hrothgar was helpless in the face of such an enemy.

The only vague hope he still held somewhere in his heart lay in a young man called Beowulf. Beowulf was the son of Egbeow, an old friend of Hrothgar's and by all accounts he'd become not just the bravest but also the cleverest warrior in the world. The last time Hrothgar had seen him he'd spent the afternoon kicking Hrothgar's shins, but then he was only three years old at the time. It brought a faint smile to Hrothgar's lips to remember this and to think that he'd forgive the bruising of all those years ago if only Beowulf would come now.

But Beowulf was a Geat. The Geats were a tribe who lived across the sea on Gotland, an island off the Swedish coast. They and the Danes had often argued and sometimes fought. They had never been the closest of allies.

Hrothgar had heard that Beowulf was in the service of the Geat king Hygelac, so he sent one of his best storytellers to Goataland and urged him to tell the stories at the court of the king in the hope that Beowulf's attention would be caught. But so far Beowulf had not risen to the challenge. If he didn't want to fight Grendel there was nothing Hrothgar could do to force him.

Hrothgar had been worried for some time that other kings, knowing how frail he was, would want to invade his lands and take over his kingdom. Of course they didn't, because if they had done they would have inherited the problem of Grendel. As no-one wanted that the land of the Danes was actually quite safe. But Hrothgar couldn't rely on that so he formed an army of coastguards to protect the borders. Some were stationed high on hillsides in lookouts which gave them views for miles in any direction. Others rode on horseback the length of the coast to challenge anyone who arrived by boat.

It was one of these coastguards, riding his horse along the beach early one morning, who noticed something off in the distance which made him stop and strain his eyes. It looked to him like a low flying, slow flying dragon. He couldn't believe it was a dragon because no-one had seen one in that part of the world in living memory, and from what he'd heard dragons preferred to fly much clearer of water than this one was doing.

Then, as he watched it coming slowly nearer, he realised it was a boat made to look like a dragon. The bowhead was carved in the shape of a dragon's head and the stern was carved to look like a tail. From a distance the wind had made the sails look like dragon's wings. The hull and masts were made of a silvery wood that reflected the early morning light and gave an eerie, shimmering quality to its movement over the waves.

When it had come as close to the shore as it could the boat's anchor was lowered and a moment later six men jumped overboard and waded through the water towards the shore.

"Halt!" the coastguard's sword was held high as a warning. "Come no closer until you've told me who you are." The one at the front, who seemed to be the leader, was rather shorter than the others and a little broader. He held his arms out wide and smiled at the coastguard as water dripped from his clothes. "Do we look like enemies?" He grinned at the others and one of them called out, "We've come for your fish!" at which they all laughed.

The coastguard was still suspicious. "You're armed with swords and shields and dressed in chainmail and battle clothes -"

"Which are weighed down with water at the moment and very heavy," the leader pointed out. The one who'd made the joke about the fish was hopping on his right leg and trying to get his left boot off. When it came off he held it upside down and a fish fell back into the water. "There's one!" he shouted.

"Let it go!" said one of the others, "it might be seen as an act of war to catch a Danish fish!" The others laughed at this but the leader signalled for them to be quiet. "Believe me," he said to the coastguard, "we're here to help you, not invade you. My name is Beowulf."

"You're Beowulf?" the coastguard said in a tone that suggested surprise rather than disbelief.

"I know what you're thinking," one of the others called out, "he got the brains and courage, we got the looks!" Beowulf ignored them as they laughed and the coastguard looked flustered as if he'd said something wrong. "They're often like this, I'm afraid," Beowulf said, "but they come in useful sometimes. Can you lead us to Hrothgar, sir?"

"It will be an honour!" the coastguard beamed. "But let me first secure your vessel." He produced a horn from under his cloak and no sooner had he blown it than a dozen other coastguards appeared as if from nowhere to be given the job of guarding Beowulf's boat until their return.

"Perhaps, on the way, you can refresh our memories as to what exactly we've come to take on here," Beowulf said.

"That, too, would be an honour," said the coastguard as they set off up the hill towards Hrothgar's castle. He led the way, with Beowulf at his side. The others, Elfrig, Eldred, Hragar, Ghorat and Anghead, the youngest, followed in single file and listened just as carefully. By the time they reached the castle they'd heard again all the old stories about Grendel, and one or two of the newer ones as well.

When they reached the top of the hill the coastguard explained that he had to return to his post, but promised that he and his colleagues would guard Beowulf's boat until his return. Beowulf knew that another reason for the coastguard's return was that their arrival could have been a trick to distract the Danes' attention from a larger invasion force.

Wulfgar was called for and when he heard who the visitors were he sent word to Hrothgar and stayed with them until a message arrived summoning the Geats into the castle.

Hrothgar was thrilled at Beowulf's arrival. They hugged like old friends and the king made all the Geats welcome in his hall. Food and drink was brought for the visitors' breakfast while Beowulf asked Hrothgar to tell him everything he knew about the monster. Beowulf's friends listened politely while they ate but couldn't understand why he needed to hear the stories yet again so soon after he'd heard them from the coastguard. But Beowulf's attention was fixed on Hrothgar to the extent that he hardly ate anything, even though he must have been hungry. Gradually they could see an expression forming on his face that they recognised: he was developing a plan.

As well as being shorter and a little stockier than the others Beowulf was also a little short sighted. This may not sound like the ideal material from which to make a great hero but it was the fact that Beowulf understood his own weaknesses that made him the warrior he was. He realised at an early age that everyone has a weakness of some kind and that the best way to defeat an enemy is to find theirs. Working on your enemy's weakness, rather than relying on brute strength, is always a better strategy.

When Hrothgar had finished talking, Beowulf sat quietly and ate. The others were still in a jolly mood but they talked more quietly now, keeping an eye and ear out for when Beowulf was ready to share his thoughts. When he finished his meal he wiped his mouth. "Excellent breakfast," he said and raised his goblet. "To our generous host and lord, Hrothgar!" The others echoed the toast. Hrothgar smiled and nodded his thanks. "It is I who should salute you," he said to Beowulf. The younger man smiled, replying, 'You can do so in the morning when we return from Heorot, victorious. In the meantime we have work to do."

Beowulf wanted to look at the hall for himself. As soon as he said this he could sense that no-one in the castle wanted to go down the path, even in broad daylight, so he and his friends went alone. As they got further away from the castle they noticed that the birdsong died down. There were probably a dozen reasons for this but they all felt it was a sign that the birds knew what happened at the bottom of the hill and were warning them to stay away.

When they reached the clearing at the edge of the forest they stood for a while and looked around them. All was still and deathly silent. Even the trees had a greyish hue about them, as if something was poisoning the land that they stood in, sucking the life and colour out of everything around.

Beowulf was the first to move towards the hall, and at his sign the others followed quietly. It had been twelve years since any human had entered the hall, and it showed. Where Grendel had smashed the door down the wind and rain had blown in, rotting the door frame and the floor at the entrance to the hall. The door itself crumpled to dust when Beowulf touched it and hundreds of insects wriggled away in panic.

There were dried bloodstains on the floor and walls. Fresher stains from rotting animal remains were scattered around the hall. Birds had pecked holes in parts of the roof. Over the years the rain had seeped in and begun to rot the wood. There were nests in the roof among the rafters. There were huge cobwebs all over the walls and ceiling, some of them with the biggest spiders any of them had ever seen. The floor was thick with crusted and dried animal droppings and dung.

They all stood, absolutely still and absolutely silent. None of them noticed anything moving but they all felt they were being watched. A scuffling sound from within the walls told them there were rats and mice living close by.

Above all, the very air in the hall smelled of decay, and of death.

"This is awful," said Eldred. Anghead was affected even more - he ran back outside and vomited.

"Awful now," Elfrig agreed as Anghead ran past, "but you can see it was a wonderful hall when it was built."

"I know, but the smell....." Eldred grimaced.

"You'll get used to it," Beowulf said, "Give me a hand here - I need to see what state these rafters are in." They helped him climb up on to the rafters, some of which were rotting quite badly but one or two were still in surprisingly good condition. Beowulf jumped up and down on them to test their strength. "Good," he said as jumped off the central rafter and then, catching hold of it as he fell, swung round and back up on to it in a way that most men simply wouldn't have the strength to do. "This will do," he smiled and the others knew from the twinkle in his eye that he was looking forward to the night.

After carefully studying the state of the hall Beowulf led his men back up the hill and suggested they sleep until supper time. "We have a long night ahead of us," he explained. "You're going to need all your strength." When they got back to the castle they followed his instructions; they had seen the evidence of carnage in the hall and knew they faced a terrible ordeal.

But he didn't go straight to bed himself. Instead he sat for another hour or so quizzing Hrothgar and other people in the castle about the monster, making sure he heard every story and found out every fact he could about the creature. The stories were in plentiful supply, the facts less so. He nodded politely but didn't say anything when time and time again he heard that the monster was hundreds of years old and could sleep for generations at a time.

Nothing lives for that long, he thought to himself. He remembered being told when he was a boy that Dragons live for a thousand years. An old sailor had told him that, and he'd heard it far away in the eastern lands where Dragons were revered, rather than reviled. But Beowulf knew that stories had a life of their own and as the stories of dragons and monsters spread so did the fear. It was the fear that lived for a thousand years, long after the creature itself was dead and gone.

It was the same here, he thought to himself as he listened to the Danes' stories. Grendel was probably older than anyone in Hrothgar's castle, but if he was as old as they believed he'd surely be frail and weak by now. Beowulf suspected that Grendel wasn't as quick or strong now as he had been when he was younger, but he would still be a dangerous enemy. When Beowulf had seen the state of the hall he knew, as always, that strength alone would not defeat the enemy. The greatest weapons Beowulf would have that night would be his speed, his wits, and the element of surprise.

He knew he wouldn't be able to sleep when he got back to his room. He lay on the bed staring at the ceiling and listening to the sounds around him, the hustle and bustle of castle life on one side, the sound of the birds through the window on the other. When he had a difficult task ahead of him he found it useful to be somewhere quiet on his own, preparing for what was to come. To think through all the possibilities and how to deal with them in advance enabled him to face a situation in a useful frame of mind: sharpened with anticipation, ready for the worst, while at the same time strangely removed from everything and relaxed.

It was something Elfrig, his dear and lifelong friend, had never understood. As far as he could see the quicker and louder you charged into a situation the more likely you were to get out again in one piece. He would never say anything to hurt his friend but Beowulf knew that it was precisely because most warriors were like Elfrig that his own approach was the more effective.

Chapter Four

At supper there was, inevitably, a certain atmosphere, a tension in the air. Everyone was trying to be cheerful and happy but everyone knew what Beowulf and his men would be facing later so they were trying not to be too cheerful and happy. No-one actually raised the subject of Grendel. The conversation across the table was a little stilted and forced, to say the least. "It's like being at someone's funeral," Hragar pointed out under his breath.

"Not ours, I hope" said Ghorat.

When Beowulf stood up at the end of the meal and thanked Hrothgar for his hospitality there was a sense of relief in the hall, as if everyone suddenly knew what to say, what to think and feel. The Geats pulled on the final layers of their armour, a mixture of chainmail and leather that would enable them to move quietly and swiftly whilst still being protected. Everyone wished them luck, shaking their hands and patting their backs, so that it took several minutes for them to say their good-byes. Hrothgar hugged each one of them. Wealtheow kissed each of Beowulf's friends in turn and gave them a small, highly polished pebble as a good luck charm. Some of them wondered if a pebble would be enough. When she came to Beowulf she pressed his pebble into his hand and told him, "You are indeed a brave young man."

"A life without courage is no life at all," he smiled. She knew what he meant and kissed him on the forehead.

The march down the hill was carried out in silence. Beowulf had ordered this before they left the castle but no-one was in any mood to talk much anyway. They knew that some of them might not walk back up the hill in the morning.

It was a clear night with almost a full moon. They could see the shapes of the trees quite clearly and as they got closer the moonlight was reflected in the bark of some trees, giving a fleeting sense of a ghostly figure watching their descent into an uncharted underworld.

As they crossed the threshold and entered the hall they heard a scurrying of rats and mice going back into the fabric of the building. Once the rodents had hidden, there was a silence so strong it was almost deafening.

The smell didn't seem to be as bad in the cool of the night. Either that, or they were more used to it by now. But when Beowulf gathered them into a circle and spoke softly they could hardly believe their ears. "We need to cover ourselves in the stuff that's on the floor," he said.

"What?" Elfrig asked.

"You heard."

"I heard, but why?"

"Think about it: what we've come to kill has, by all accounts, been here every night for the last twelve years. He knows what this place smells like and his sense of smell is

probably far greater than ours. If we're sitting here waiting for him all nice and clean he'll smell us a mile away."

There were groans and protests, even though they knew he was, of course, quite right. "But most of what's on the floor is ordure," said Anghead, who looked as if he might be sick again.

"I know."

"Excrement!"

"Ordure, excrement, faeces, droppings, call it what you like, you're going to have to cover yourselves with it."

And so they did. And as they rolled around the floor the groans began to be replaced with giggles and pretend vomiting noises. Then they had to smother it all over their faces and into their hair. As Beowulf vigorously smeared the remains of a dead rat all over Elfrig's back his friend told him, "If this doesn't work you are personally going to scrape the muck off my chain mail!"

"If this doesn't work," Beowulf replied, "you'll probably have to scrape what's left of me off the walls."

And then they waited. Sitting on the floor, leaning against the wall in the darkest edges of the hall, they were relaxed but ready for anything. After a while, Eldred whispered to Beowulf, "Remind me again: what are we doing here?" Some of the others laughed abruptly. It was a thought which had crossed their minds once or twice during the day.

"You're here to collect a reward," Beowulf reminded them.

"Partly," Elfrig agreed. "But mainly we're here because you're here. So why are you here?"

Beowulf sighed. "Because many years ago, long before I was born, my father was accused of murdering a prince. He was innocent but couldn't prove it, so he ran away. There were bounty hunters after him and the only place he could find refuge was here, in the land of the Danes, under the protection of the young king Hrothgar. Eventually they realised it wasn't my father who killed the prince and he was allowed to return. From that day to this my family have owed Hrothgar a certain debt, a certain allegiance."

"But didn't your father pay tribute to Hrothgar in gold?" Ghorat asked. "That's what I heard, anyway."

"Of course he paid tribute," Beowulf replied, "but there's more to it than that. There are some things you can't just pay for with money, you have to do something in return. There comes a point in every man's life when he has the chance to do something that will mark him out as different among men. If you don't leave your mark in this life how will anyone know you were here after you're gone? This is my chance to do that, and since you're with me it's yours as well. If we succeed tonight we'll do more than collect a reward, and more than repay Hrothgar's kindness to my father."

With that Beowulf climbed up on to the central rafter and took up position in the centre of the hall at its highest point. The others spread themselves around, leaning against the walls in the darkest shadows of the dark hall.

And they were silent. They didn't talk and they hardly moved. They sat, looking and listening. Their eyes adjusted to the darkness and their ears tuned in to the sounds of the forest so that they almost became at one with the world around them. They became a living, breathing part of Heorot.

Above them, on the central rafter that held the roof in place, Beowulf sat with a straight back and his legs crossed so that they didn't dangle over the rafter. He too was so silent, so still, that he became part of the hall itself. The others, down on the floor, knew where he was but couldn't see him. It was almost as if he had made himself invisible.

They knew Grendel was coming long before they could hear him. They heard slight changes in the noises outside and in the fabric of the building as the creatures who lived there sensed his approach. The sounds of the forest that they'd become more and more aware of as they sat and listened in silence died away and the world became truly, almost deafeningly, silent. It seemed as if the world was holding its breath.

And then they heard it. A soft, slightly wheezy breathing, like someone with a very heavy cold. Then they noticed the sound he made as he walked, almost as if he'd broken a leg and was dragging it behind him. They all realised at the same time, before they'd even set eyes on him, that this creature was more comfortable swimming through the swamp than he was walking on dry land: he dragged his feet rather than lifting them when he walked.

As they realised this their hearts felt lighter and started to beat a little more quickly with excitement as they anticipated the fight to come. They knew, still without saying a word to each other, that they had found an advantage over him that the other poor humans who'd faced him had not had chance to: however strong, powerful and savage he might be, he couldn't move on dry land quite as easily and quickly as they could. He couldn't jump and leap the way they could.

A moment later he crossed the clearing and then he stopped. They couldn't see him yet but they sensed him looking around carefully as if something made him suspicious. Then they heard him sniff the air. Three short sniffs and one long one as he tried to work out what had happened around the hall earlier that day. They knew that he could tell that some humans had been there. They held their breath, suddenly aware that this creature's sense of smell was so strong that even their breath would tell him they were there. And as the creature moved forward across the threshold and entered the darkness of the hall they knew how clever and how right Beowulf had been to insist they make themselves smell as bad as the hall.

They could all see him now, and he was as fearsome as they had been told. About eight feet tall he looked like a cross between a giant and a wolf. His mouth was pushed forward by his long jaw and they could see the long rows of sharp teeth as he snarled with suspicion. That was the point at which all of them, having held their breath as he entered and they got their first good look at him, quietly let the breath escape from their lungs. They were as quiet as they could be but the sound of one man's breath escaping was enough to alert him.

He stopped. They froze. He cocked his head slightly to one side to listen and sniffed the air again. He held his breath, gathering the information from around him. He must have felt it was safe because then he started to move towards the centre of the hall.

They could all see now what they'd heard as he approached. He walked on dry land by dragging one leg after the other. As he did so they could see the slight trail of swamp and mud that he left behind him, in much the same way as a slug leaves a trail behind it.

But this creature was no slug. He moved swiftly across the floor towards the back of the hall, sensing there was something to eat somewhere around. But just as he walked under the central rafter Beowulf dropped the pebble Wealtheow had given him to the creature's right. Grendel stopped as the pebble hit the floor and then moved towards it. When it stopped moving he bent down to pick it up and that was when Beowulf dropped like a silent stone from nowhere and landed on Grendel's back, one arm instantly around the creature's neck, his legs around its waist and his free arm wielding his sword into Grendel's back.

Grendel, howling in surprise and anger, reared up like a stallion to shrug Beowulf off. Beowulf had expected this and was hanging on tight with one arm and both legs, his other arm sticking his sword into Grendel's leathery skin with blows that were not just heavier than any Grendel had felt before but also faster, sharper and repeated over and over again. Each thrust of Beowulf's sword hurt Grendel more than anything else he had ever felt. He screamed as the sword cut his flesh and his blood started to gush from the wounds.

He didn't like this but he didn't know what to do about it. It seemed as if this thing on his back was stronger than any creature he'd come across before as well as being more agile than he was. His instincts told him to fall back on to the floor on top of it and crush the life out of it.

Beowulf realised what Grendel was trying to do as he felt the monster's body weight shift. As Grendel leaned so far back that he couldn't pull himself up again Beowulf let go, fell to the ground and quickly rolled out of the way so that when Grendel landed he fell straight down on his own back, winding himself quite badly.

In the moment or so it took Grendel to gather his thoughts and get his breath back Beowulf jumped heavily onto his chest, knocking the wind out of his lungs again, and kicked him in the face. The blow to the head jolted Grendel in more ways than one and he realised that this creature would have to be dealt with immediately. A deafening roar filled the hall as he curled forward to sit up and reached to grab hold of Beowulf at the same time. As he reached for one of Beowulf's arms Beowulf shouted "NOW!" and the other five launched themselves from the dark edges of the hall towards the monster.

Beowulf was holding Grendel's arm tightly with both of his and the others were swinging their swords into Grendel's skin as he lurched from side to side, trying to free his arm from Beowulf's grip. Elfrig leaped unseen towards Grendel's back and with absolute precision sliced his sword downwards beside the creature's spine. Grendel screamed with something between the squeal of a hog and the roar of a bear. Lashing out with his free arm he grabbed hold of Ghorat's head.

It seemed to the others as if the world froze for a second. They watched in silent horror as Grendel's hand enveloped Ghorat's head. They were helpless as Ghorat's eyes widened and the creature's fingers tightened until the blood was oozing between them, followed a second later by the pulped brain. Ghorat's head was completely crushed. His body fell to the floor.

Beowulf screamed in fury. Sheathing his sword he took hold of the monster's arm with both of his and he ran behind Grendel and underneath the arm so that it was twisted round and up behind the creature. Standing behind Grendel, Beowulf kicked upwards with all the force he could manage right between the creature's legs. Grendel yelped and crumpled forward with the pain, but Beowulf kept a tight grip so that as Grendel crumpled forward he pulled on his own arm, causing himself even more pain. And still the others were raining furious blows on Grendel with their swords, desperate now to punish him for killing their friend.

And then what Beowulf had been waiting for - what he'd carefully thought through while he was lying on his bed in the castle - started to happen: Beowulf had realised during the day that their most powerful weapon would be fear. Not their own, but the ability to create it in Grendel. If he'd never felt it before he wouldn't know how to deal with it. And now, with swords cutting into him from every angle and his own blood spilling onto the floor, Grendel began to realise that this was a situation he'd never been in before. Until now every other creature Grendel had come up against in his entire life had either been killed more or less instantly, or had managed somehow to get away. But this was different. These humans were the first to actually fight back. Grendel realised that he'd never really been in a fight before, and then he began to understand that a fight can be lost as well as won.

Finding it impossible to shake off his attackers, and feeling more pain than he'd ever felt in his life, Grendel began to be afraid. It started in the pit of his stomach and his slow-witted mind wondered what the feeling was. When he didn't recognise the feeling that made him anxious and that in turn made the feeling stronger. From there it seemed to rush through his mind and body, taking him over completely and making him just want to go home, back to his lair. He didn't understand these thoughts and he didn't like them. Something told him that the only way he could get rid of them was to go away from them and that's all he wanted to now. He'd had enough to eat, he didn't need anything else, he just wanted to go. But they wouldn't let him, and they were surprisingly strong.

All he wanted to do now was get away and he started to drag himself towards the entrance to the hall. But the sharp, painful blows of swords were still hitting him, slicing through his skin, and his arm was still held twisted up his back. Afraid that he wouldn't even make it to the entrance he started to panic, trying to twist and wriggle out of the grip he was held in. As he reached the door frame he swatted at the others with his free arm and then used it to grab the rotting door frame and pull himself through it. But two of those he'd swatted away now joined with Beowulf in gripping his other arm. Others were now striking at his legs with their swords, trying to cut them from under him. He summoned all the strength he had left in his body and tried to hurl himself through the door frame. He pulled with such force that an almighty pain seared through his body as he felt a ripping sensation around his shoulder. It came with a horrible cracking sound that told Beowulf the creature had dislocated its shoulder. In an instant Beowulf had let go of the arm, taken out his sword, raised it above his head and swung it with all his strength and weight down through the shoulder, cutting the arm completely free and filling the air with blood.

The most unearthly, chilling scream of pain split the night air as Grendel fell forward and landed in the clearing. Those still holding the arm fell on to their backs with the arm across them, Grendel's blood splattered all over their faces and armour.

Beowulf had landed with a hefty thump on his knee. He knelt, slightly winded, on the floor of the hall with his sword stuck into the floorboards, such was the force with which he'd cut through the shoulder. Panting and sweating, they smiled at each other in relief, knowing their ordeal was over. They hadn't killed the monster, but they knew they'd inflicted a mortal wound and it would bleed to death during the course of the day.

They felt exhausted after such an intense and gruelling fight, but they summoned what strength they had left and found a meat hook in the kitchens, on which they stuck the monster's severed arm. Then Beowulf climbed on Elfrig's shoulders and fastened the hook above the door frame so that anyone who passed would see that they had won their fight. Then, not wishing to disrupt the castle at such an early hour, they went back inside the hall and slept, with two of them at a time keeping watch. They believed Grendel would be in too much pain to attack them again, but there was no point in taking chances.....

Chapter Five

The piercing shriek that Grendel had given as his arm was cut off had travelled through the night air and was heard by many in the castle. Some were woken up by it. Others had not been able to sleep for thinking about what might be happening in Heorot. All were chilled to the bone by the noise they heard. All of them assumed the cry was a human's response to what Grendel had done to them.

Once dawn had broken the light made it safe enough for six soldiers to be ordered to bring back what remained of Beowulf and his men. They walked down the hill in silence but when they got to the clearing the one at the front held his arm out to stop the others. For a second they thought he'd seen something terrible still lurking in the shadows of the hall, but when they followed his gaze and saw the arm hung above the doorway they were elated.

They ran into the hall and greeted Beowulf and his men like long lost brothers, hugging them, slapping them on the back, almost dancing with delight. Then they saw the remains of Ghorat and fell respectfully silent. They insisted on carrying his body back to the castle and led the way back up the hill in a more sombre mood.

The mood in the castle was equally mixed. Hrothgar gave a moving speech in which he pointed out that Ghorat would be the last of many humans to have been killed by

Grendel but he had not died in vain. His death had helped to liberate Hrothgar's people from the tyranny of the monster; and his courage, and those of his comrades, would be rewarded in many many ways, starting with a party in Heorot itself that very night. For his part Beowulf pointed out that Ghorat would have celebrated as much as anyone if he'd survived the night so they mustn't let his death spoil the mood of jubilation that began to sweep through the castle and beyond.

For the rest of the day servants worked like bees, buzzing around the castle and the hall and up and down the hill between, cleaning and repairing the hall and preparing food and drink for the first party in Heorot in many many years. Visitors came to the castle throughout the day as word spread of Beowulf's victory: noblemen from all around brought jewellery and weapons for the Geats. Poorer people brought what little they could afford to give - a bunch of carrots or a cabbage - as a token of their gratitude to Beowulf, and all who came were made very welcome and invited to stay for the party.

As for the party, no-one could remember such singing and dancing, such joy on the faces of every single person in the hall. It was as if a great weight had been lifted from the shoulders of everyone there and they all looked and felt years younger as a result. Everyone felt such a huge sense of relief and happiness. Even Hrothgar danced, and as he did so people realised they hadn't seen him dance since the last party in the hall. They'd never expected to see him so much as smile again, and yet here he was, back to his old self.

Well, almost back to his old self. The years had taken their toll on him and he wasn't as young or as fit as he had been, so no-one was surprised when he announced, in the early hours of the morning, that he'd had enough and would have to go to bed. Immediately servants started to clear things away and guests began to thank the king and leave for home. Hrothgar and Wealtheow were accompanied up the hill by Beowulf and his men, while Wulfgar asked six soldiers to stay behind to keep an eye on the hall once everyone else had gone.

In no time at all the lively, noisy hall had fallen once more into peace and quiet. The soldiers asked to stay behind were happy to, of course, but they were tired, having been at the party and having had perhaps a little too much to eat and drink. Then again, they knew better than to allow themselves to fall asleep all at the same time. One of the older soldiers, a man called Beornwald, pointed out that, strictly speaking, no-one could be certain Grendel was dead. He'd lost his arm and was badly wounded, that much they knew for sure, but what if he was still alive? If he was still alive, in pain and angry, as wounded animals often were, then he might come back to the hall now that the noise had died down. The others agreed it was not worth taking risks and decided to draw straws: the one who drew the shortest straw would take first watch while the rest of them slept. Two hours each would see them safely through to the afternoon.

Beornwald volunteered to go outside to get some blades of grass of differing lengths. As he walked away from the hall to the edge of the clearing where the forest began he was struck by how quiet it was. He couldn't hear a sound. Not a single animal, bird or human voice, and the sky was as black as he'd ever seen it. It almost seemed as if the stars themselves were afraid to look down, and at that thought a shiver ran through him. To his surprise he realised he was uncomfortable standing alone at the edge of the clearing. He was beginning to feel afraid. He was annoyed with himself at this and to rid himself of the fear he stood with a completely straight back, took a deep breath and stared out past the edge of the clearing into the darkness beyond. But this didn't entirely work. As he stood staring into the darkness he became more and more uncomfortable about the silence that greeted him. He couldn't see anything in the darkness, but he had an uncomfortable feeling that something in the darkness could see him.

Trying to shake off these silly imaginings, he went back into the hall and was dismayed to draw the shortest straw. The others saw the look on his face and teased him about it as they sorted out blankets and settled down to sleep in the middle of the hall. Within minutes they were quiet and probably asleep. The light from the torches on the walls cast strange shadows across the hall and from time to time a draught of wind made the flames flicker and the whole inside of the hall seemed to change shape.

He was tired, and bored. He began to whistle to himself but a sharp voice whispered "Shut up!" from the middle of the hall so he did.

A while later he began to hum very quietly to himself but another voice barked "Be quiet!". He couldn't understand how anyone had even heard him, he was humming very softly, but again he stopped and the hall was silent.

It was the silence that was the worst thing about keeping watch. He realised it would have been more sensible for two of them to have kept watch together. Two of them would have kept each other awake, after all. Two of them would have meant he had someone to pass the time with, to talk to. But then two of them would have still had to talk to each other, he realised, and would still have annoyed the others.

So there he was, on his own, bored and rather lonely. And tired. So very tired. So tired his eyelids were heavy and started to droop but as soon as they did he snapped himself awake. He mustn't sleep. He knew he must not sleep. But as soon as the mere thought of sleep entered his mind he felt so much better, so much happier, because all he really wanted to do was sleep....... but he mustn't!

He jolted upright again and opened his eyes as wide as he could. But doing so was hard work and he closed them to rest them and then realised of course! That's what he could do: he wouldn't fall asleep but he would rest with his eyes closed. Yes, that would be fine, just to stay awake but rest with his eyes closed. So he closed his eyes to rest but stay awake.

And he stayed awake with his eyes closed for a few minutes.

And then he fell asleep.

And that was a mistake.

It was a mistake because just as evil men have mothers, so do evil creatures. And Grendel's mother was still alive.

Realising the extent of his wounds after the fight with Beowulf, Grendel had done the only thing he could think to do and sought out his mother. He had struggled through the forest, crawled across the swamp and limped across the moors all the way to her lair. By the time he'd reached the moors he'd found the pain was a little more bearable if he held his remaining hand tightly over the wound at his shoulder, but Beowulf's men had cut his legs so badly with their swords that he struggled to walk. When he stumbled he didn't have an arm to hold out to help him keep his balance so he fell hard onto the ground, which brought back the agony in his shoulder.

It had taken him all day and all his remaining strength to reach her, and not long after he'd slithered down into her lair he died in her arms. She was heartbroken. And furious. She could see that no animal had done this, the wound was too precise. This had been done by humans, and humans would pay for this. Even monsters love their children.

Descended as she was from serpents, she had no legs, but two strong arms and strong muscles all the way along the length of her body. She had slithered and crawled across the moors, glided through the slimy swamp and climbed through the forest. When necessary she could even coil herself tightly and then flex her muscles so that she would leap forward, the narrow length of her body enabling her to remain airborne for a few seconds, as if gliding through the air.

She had climbed and crawled the last part of her journey, following the scent her son had left in the forest every night for the last twelve years until she had reached the clearing where the hall Heorot stood. There she had waited, listening to the sound of the murderers enjoying themselves, watching them leave the hall until she knew there just a few of them. Even when all was quiet she waited, watching as one of those who remained in the hall had come out into the clearing and stood just a short distance in front of her, trying to be brave.

And now she had waited long enough. Long enough for them to think there was no danger. She moved slowly and silently towards the door and held her breath for a moment, listening. One of them was snoring on the other side of the door. She knew humans well enough to know that if one of them had been awake they would have complained about the noise. They were all asleep.

As is often the case, the mother was more subtle than her son. She stretched up and slowly, carefully, opened the door, letting it swing in on its hinges, taking in the sight that presented itself to her. Five men sleeping close together in the centre of the hall, another asleep against the wall.

She coiled herself tightly and then sprang forward, leaping across the hall towards the unsuspecting soldiers. Her talons were long, black and razor sharp and she sank them into the sleeping bodies, tearing all five of them to shreds within seconds, cutting them open from their stomachs in all directions. The screams woke Beornwald, who leapt to his feet and ran with his sword towards her. She didn't even do him the courtesy of looking at him: she stretched out her arm and he ran straight on to her talons and was killed instantly.

Her fury and anger spent, she remained in the silent hall for a while, quenching her thirst by drinking some of the blood she had spilt. When she was ready to leave she took one of the soldiers and hurled him up to the roof. His body landed over the central rafter, almost exactly where Beowulf had waited for her son. She didn't know this, of course, she just thought it would serve as a warning to other humans. She left the hall as quietly as she had entered and faded into the surrounding darkness.

Chapter Six

When the remains of the soldiers were discovered in the morning a cloud fell on the castle that was darker than any night sky. It seemed as if there was no escape from the terror after all. Beowulf couldn't understand it. "The arm was cut clean off," he said to Hrothgar. "He couldn't have lived more than a few hours, surely?"

"You saw how strong he is," Hrothgar shrugged.

"And you saw the arm. How could anything survive that?"

"There is another possibility," one of Hrothgar's thanes said. "There's a man lives out on the moors on a smallholding he's made there. He's lived there for as long as I can remember and he's a good age. He was here last night, telling anyone who'd listen that he's heard tell of more than one monster around the moors."

"Oh, wonderful!" Hrothgar wailed, "there's a family of them!"

"He only spoke of one more, I'm sure of it," the thane said. The servants who'd been working at the party were called into the hall and some of them said that they, too, had heard what the man had said, but had thought little of it at the time.

"Did you not think this might have been significant?" Hrothgar asked. No-one could remember him speaking so sarcastically before. There was an uncomfortable silence for a moment, and then one of the young girls coughed politely.

"With respect, sir, I think we all thought he'd just had a bit too much to drink. You know what some people are like when they've had a few, they like to pretend they know more than they do."

This was true, they all knew. But if the old man was right this would begin to explain what happened the night before. Grendel was not alone. There was at least one more, as dreadful as he was. It would seem that, in killing Grendel, Beowulf had brought a new kind of terror upon them. All the worse, perhaps, for being caused by anger and driven by revenge.

Beowulf was undeterred. "This proves we killed Grendel," he reasoned. "This was an act of revenge. So now all we have to do is find the other one."

Hrothgar was dismayed. "But we don't even know where it lives!"

"But it must live somewhere within reach of here," Beowulf pointed out. "It must have found Grendel's body some time yesterday, which means it can't be far away. Lend us some horses and we'll find it."

Hrothgar gave them each a white charger, the finest horses the Danes had, and almost immediately they set off down the hill and into the forest. It didn't take them long to find the tracks that Grendel had left as he struggled away from Heorot. Dried blood confirmed they were his. They ended at the edge of the swamp where he'd sunk into the mud.

"Not much to tell us here," Beowulf said. "We need to find the man who lives on the moors."

Elfrig's eyesight was stronger than Beowulf's and he could see further. "See that?" he asked Beowulf and pointed across the swamp. Beowulf shook his head. "There's a hole just level with the surface on the other side. It looks like a foxhole but it's too low down, too near the mud for a fox to have dug it. They prefer to be drier."

By now the others could see it but Beowulf still couldn't. "Lead the way," he told Elfrig, "but as quietly as you can, all of you, and keep your wits about you: the other one might be anywhere."

By the time they reached the far side of the swamp they could all see that this was no ordinary hole. Beowulf sensed this was the entrance to Grendel's lair and insisted on going alone. The others waited on horseback as he climbed down the bank of the swamp and peered into the hole for a moment before disappearing into it.

He quickly found that the tunnel was just wide enough for him to wriggle along, and too narrow to allow him to turn round. It also got very dark very quickly. If he did come face to face with anything he'd have to fight it head on without being able to see it.

The tunnel meandered up and down as it went underground so that the mud from the swamp stayed in pools in parts of the tunnel but didn't get as far as the lair itself.

The air was stale, but at least he could breathe. The climb had been hard work and taken longer than he'd expected. He knew that although he'd tried to be silent his breathing would have been heard by anything further along the tunnel. Anything that was there would be waiting for him.

Finally, he reached the opening to the lair itself. He paused and listened, holding his breath. It was completely dark, and he couldn't hear anything. He pulled himself out of the tunnel as quickly as he could, rolling onto the floor and then springing to his feet. As he leaped up he swung his sword all around him so that anything approaching him would be hit.

There was nothing.

Again he paused and listened carefully. Not a sound could be heard, but there was a horrible smell. It was the same smell that had filled Heorot when they first went there, but it was far worse here because it was contained within a smaller space. He knew for certain this was Grendel's lair.

He took a few steps forward but then tripped over something and fell to the floor. Instinctively he twisted to one side so he didn't land on his own sword and as he hit the ground he swung it above him but found nothing. He lay on his back, waiting for his attacker to pounce. The silence and stillness were as strong as the darkness. Nothing happened.

He shuffled on his back slightly to where he had fallen over. His boot found something on the ground, quite still but too soft to be a rock. It was a creature, he was certain, but when he kicked it there was no reaction. It was dead. Or pretending to be. Holding his sword in his right hand he felt the dead object with his left and realised it was the remains of a human being. The head was intact but large parts of the rest of the body had been torn off or torn open. Grendel didn't like the heads.

Grendel, or what was left of him by now, obviously wasn't there. Beowulf crawled back along the hole and rejoined his friends. As he climbed back onto his horse Elfrig wet a finger and held it up to see which way the wind was blowing. "Would you mind riding upwind of us, illustrious leader?" He asked. Beowulf saw the expression on the others' faces. They were sniggering. Rather childishly, Beowulf thought.

"Oh, such gratitude!" He said. "You've no idea how bad it was down there."

"And you've no idea how bad it is up here!" said Elfrig, and the others laughed.

They left the swamp and found themselves on moorland that was as bleak as the forest was dark. The horses were skittish about riding over such soft and boggy ground. The Geats soon realised the horses had their own sense of which ground was more secure so they allowed the animals to lead the way.

The horses led them to the safest, and most fertile, parts of the land. It was not long before they could see a small settlement of houses built on the hardest land of the moors, but as they got closer it seemed that the settlement had been all but abandoned. There was one house which had smoke rising from a fire within. It was made of wattle and daub, the weaving of branches around a wooden frame then covered with a mixture of earth and dung. It was little more than a hovel in the centre of an enclosure of land in which the owner kept a few pigs and sheep and grew vegetables. A smallholding rather than a farm.

"Who on earth would choose to live here?" Eldred asked.

"We can't all choose where we live," said Beowulf as he dismounted from his horse. "We must do the best with what we have. And anyone who lives here must have his wits about him."

"I have," said the smallholder approaching the fence from the other side. "My father built this when he married my mother. In those days there were other people here, but now there's only me and my animals."

"You've lived here all your life?" Beowulf asked. The man nodded. Beowulf looked at his face but it was difficult to tell his age. A lifetime of living in such harsh conditions could make even the youngest of men look old.

"No doubt you've seen many things," said Beowulf .

"Aye," the man smiled, "I've seen things you wouldn't believe." Then he looked deep into Beowulf's eyes and said, "You're looking for something you haven't seen but you wonder if I have."

"Have you?" asked Beowulf.

"How do I know?" the man smiled, "you haven't told me what you're looking for. But judging by the state you're in I'd say you were keen to find it!" The others laughed at this. Beowulf smiled.

"You know we killed Grendel," Beowulf said and the man nodded. "But apparently there's more than one."

The man laughed with a snort. "I did try to warn people. I've never seen more than one at a time, although my father said he often saw two together. But I know I've seen two. They used to say the other one is Grendel's mother."

"The mother." Beowulf hadn't thought of such a possibility, but he realised the implications. "So having killed the son we now need to kill the mother..."

"Before she kills you," the other man finished the sentence. "All right then," he took a deep breath, "let me ask you a question. What is it that can turn a coward into a brave man and a brave man into a fool?"

"That's not a question, that's a riddle," said Elfrig. "We don't have time to play games!"

"Don't be rude!" Beowulf snapped and turned back to the man. "My apologies, sir, my friend is impatient."

"Your friend can't afford to be," the man looked at Elfrig but spoke to Beowulf. "I ask not for fun but for a reason. If you haven't got the wit to answer my riddle you haven't got the wit to fight the mother."

He turned back to Beowulf as Beowulf said, "Wine."

"Good," said the man. "So tell me what it is that you can't see but you can watch it tear the world apart."

"The north wind," said Beowulf, and the smallholder smiled.

"So look to the north," he said. "Half a day's journey on foot from here, less by horse. Cross the moor and then go uphill into the forest. Where it seems the wind has done its worst is where you must do your best," he said and turned to walk away.

"Aren't you going to wish us luck?" Elfrig was a little irritated. He knew he'd been rude but he hated being shown to be in the wrong, especially in front of others.

"Luck has nothing to do with it," the smallholder called over his shoulder, "but I wish you success. Or a quick death," he added and went inside.

"Well, that was cheerful!" said Anghead.

"Useful," said Beowulf. "We should try to get there before dark."

They rode off in the direction the old man had told them. For the first hour or so the terrain was flat and bleak. There were bushes of prickly gorse and a handful of wind-bent trees scattered over the moorland. Their twisted shapes reminded the Geats of Grendel and seemed to be watching them on their journey.

Gradually the land climbed upwards and seemed to be more welcoming. The trees were more frequent and less wind-beaten; the grass was greener and richer. The land was fed by streams that the horses either jumped easily or drank from thirstily. As they rode on they could see deer roaming freely, a sure sign that this land was safer for all, and they entered a forest of pine trees that smelled so fresh it seemed as if it couldn't possibly harbour anything evil.

But as they reached the far side of the forest they saw immediately what the smallholder had been talking about. They drew their horses to a halt and stared in silence at an extraordinary sight.

The rest of the forest had been flattened by a powerful wind. Hundreds, perhaps thousands, of trees lay on their sides, criss-crossed over each other like lattice work. And every one of them was completely without leaves. The trunks of the trees were grey, lifeless, dead. they were so devoid of life they looked more like stone than wood. It was a terrifying reminder of the power of nature, all the more so because they'd come across it so suddenly and unexpectedly.

"The wind did this?" Hragar's voice broke the silence after a moment.

"I hope so," said Beowulf. "I'd hate to meet the human who could have done this."

They couldn't ride the horses any further so they dismounted and stood beside them for a moment.

Anghead began to tether his to one of the trees but Beowulf told him not to. "They're well trained and good natured. They'll wait for us. If we tether them they can't escape, and if we don't come back they may need to," he pointed out.

As they climbed onto the first of the trees they realised they could walk from one to another across the whole forest without touching the ground. Holding their arms out to balance themselves they walked towards the centre.

It took about ten minutes to reach the heart of the fallen forest, and right in the middle they found something else they'd never seen before. A huge old oak tree had been uprooted and lay on its side with the others. But the hole that had been left as it was pulled, roots and all, from the ground had been worked on. Someone or something had dug and burrowed further down until the hole was so deep none of the men standing at the edge could see how far down this hole reached. There was no way of seeing where it ended, if it ended at all.

"I think we've found what we were told to look for," said Beowulf as he peered down.

"I think you might be right," said Elfrig. "Would you like to go first?" he smiled.

"I think I should go alone," Beowulf replied.

"I think I should come with you," Elfrig shook his head.

"There probably isn't room for two of us," Beowulf said. "If this is like the tunnel that led to Grendel's lair it would be difficult for two of us to be in such a confined space. We'd get in each other's way." He looked up and pointed to the trees where they'd left the horses. "If I'm not back by the time the sun has moved over those trees then you have a choice: you can come down to try to rescue me or give me up for dead and get away before she gets you."

"We won't leave you," Hragar said.

"You may have to," Beowulf replied as he climbed off the tree they were standing on and into the hole. He sat for a moment at the edge of the hole, trying to decide which way to go down. Head first with his sword at the ready but possibly an uncomfortable landing, or feet first and have a vital second or so less to see what was waiting for him at the bottom. Then again, if he landed on his feet he would be more able to move quickly. He opted for feet first and started to lower himself down, holding on to a branch as he did so and grimacing to the others.

But the branch was too dry to hold his weight. It snapped with a loud crack and the next thing he knew he was falling, falling faster and faster down into the hole. He banged his shoulders as he skidded and rocked from side to side, covering himself in slimy clay mud as he went all the way down before landing with a thump at the bottom, a long way down.

His head hurt and so did his back but there wasn't time to feel sorry for himself. Almost unconsciously, without really understanding why, he stuck what was left of the branch he was still holding in the mud behind him and sprang back up looking around him. The only light was from the hole above. He stepped forward into the darkness because he realised that while he stood in the light he couldn't see beyond it, but anything else there could clearly see him.

He moved forward, holding his sword at the ready, glad that he could see a little. Then his heart seemed to leap into his mouth. Grendel was lying on the ground in front of him. He lifted his sword ready to strike but then realised that Grendel was quite still. He was dead.

Beowulf realised Grendel had struggled in pain to reach this lair, to die here. And there had to be a reason why he wanted to die here: he wanted to be with his mother. It was natural enough, Beowulf reasoned, and he almost felt sorry for Grendel in his final, painful hours. But then he heard a snuffling, shuffling sound from across the floor. He couldn't quite see what it was, but he knew what it was.

She slithered forward a little and he could see her more clearly. And she was horrible. She stared at him and he stared back at her, unable to look away. It would have been stupid to look away.

The son, he realised, had been little more than a wild oaf. Overlarge and small-brained, strong but not intelligent, Grendel had roamed the woods looking for food and possibly companionship with the same gut instincts as other wild beasts. But what stood in front of Beowulf now was altogether different and altogether more frightening. She probably lacked the brute strength of her son but more than made up for that with intelligence, and it was the intelligence with which she stared at him that made Beowulf so uncomfortable. Here was a creature who understood her surroundings rather than simply responding instinctively to them. He could see in her eyes the intelligence at work, weighing him up and thinking things through. He could see the menace in her eyes and on her face and knew that for the first, and he hoped only, time in his life he was in the presence of sheer evil.

He took a step towards her and smiled. The way in which she recoiled slightly told him all he needed to know: she knew more about humans than humans would ever know about her, and she knew what a smile meant. He smiled again and this time she didn't recoil but she looked more closely into his eyes. She couldn't understand why he was smiling and it made her uncomfortable, Beowulf could see. But what he needed to find out was if she understood speech.

"You don't frighten me," he whispered and smiled again, and again she reacted slightly. "I saw what you did to those men in the hall," he spoke a little louder now, "but you won't do that to me." He began to rock slightly from left to right on the balls of his feet, his sword waving slightly in front of him as he did so. "I wasn't afraid of him," he nodded towards Grendel's corpse, "and I'm not afraid of you. And do you know why?" He wasn't sure she understood, but he thought she'd get a sense of what he was saying. She was beginning to move slightly herself, as if she was anticipating his movements and preparing to strike. They stared into each other's eyes across the dark space, gently swaying from side to side as if mirroring each other, and he began to goad her, taunting her, daring her to strike.

"Your son was a beast," he spoke softly but clearly, "nothing more." He paused for a moment before adding, "A wild and stupid beast with plenty of strength, but not the brains to use it." He paused again. "Men would call him an oaf..... an idiot.......... a fool............ and in the end a weak fool..... easily frightened as it turned out." The look on her face told him she did understand, and his words were having the desired effect.

"All we needed to do was to actually fight back," he continued, "to stand up to him... we just held on to him and he was frightened.... started to panic.... wanted to go." He paused again before adding "I didn't even need a sword!" He suddenly stuck his own sword into the wall behind him to his right and held his left arm out wide. Then, as he raised his right hand into the air he said, "All I needed to do was SWIPE!" This last word was shouted as his arm swept downwards, miming the action of cutting Grendel's arm off.

Even if she didn't understand the words he'd been speaking, she understood the action and it told her that here, in front of her, was the human who had killed her son. Realising this produced a rush of anger that swept through her and propelled her forward, screaming monstrously as she leapt towards him.

As she sprang forward he spun to his right, turning full circle and scooping up his sword as he did so. He'd needed her to leap towards him suddenly, angrily, and he'd staked his life on being quicker than her.

The instant she leapt she saw him move and knew she'd been tricked. She was now hurtling at great speed towards the broken branch that was sticking out of the wall straight in front of her. She tried to grab hold of the branch and push herself away from it but she'd leaped with such force and fury there wasn't time and as she landed straight on it she screamed, as much in anger as in pain. She screamed again as Beowulf's sword fell down on her with such force that it almost cut her in half. She twisted and turned to face him as the blood gushed from her wound and the look of absolute hatred stayed for ever on her face as he sliced his sword through her neck and cut the head clean off.

Turning to Grendel he kicked the body onto its side, lifted his sword and struck the neck, hacking three or four times until the head was completely severed. Then, sheathing his sword, he lifted both heads by the hair and began to climb back up the tunnel.

Above ground the others had heard the scream and anxiously called down to him. "I'm fine," he called back, "but I don't know how long it will take me to get out of here."

It was a struggle climbing back up, using his arms and legs to support his body weight as he tried to balance both heads in his arms at the same time. When they could see what he was trying to do they told him to throw the heads up and they caught them, laughing grimly as they popped out of the tunnel into their arms. Then, holding on to each other, they formed a human chain and reached down to pull Beowulf the rest of the way up the tunnel.

The horses had been frightened by the screams but torn between their fear and their loyalty had not gone far. They soon came back when called by reassuring voices.

By now Beowulf's friends were also splattered with mud from the tunnel and felt almost as tired as he felt on the journey home. They rode carefully through the creeping darkness and into the night towards Hrothgar's castle.

They rode all night and reached the castle just as dawn was breaking, their white chargers coming out of the forest and winding up the path like four-legged ghosts. By now the Geats were so tired they hardly moved and could themselves have been mistaken for dead.

But as they approached the castle they straightened up and held high the heads of the two dead monsters. The watchmen saw and raised the alarm and the gates opened to allow them in as people rushed from their beds to greet them

The Geats were used to the mud and the blood they were coated in, but those who greeted them were struck by the smell and, delighted as they were to see them again alive and well, kept a polite distance. They applauded rather than giving the Geats the hugs and kisses they were expecting. Even Hrothgar tactfully suggested that baths might be in order before a celebratory breakfast.

Chapter Seven

Over breakfast it was decided that there would be another party in the hall to celebrate Beowulf's victory. So while he and his men slept for the rest of the day, the preparations were made. The hall was cleaned, the walls and door repaired again, and more food and drink was prepared than could ever be consumed in one night, even by Geats and Danes.

When the Geats awoke they bathed and dressed in new clothes provided by Hrothgar. When they presented themselves in Hrothgar's hall they were applauded and ceremoniously presented with gift upon gift upon gift. The chargers that had taken them to the mother's lair were theirs now, along with trunks of armour and jewellery, swords and shields of the most intricate and exquisite craftsmanship. They were even given a second boat to take their rewards back home across the sea. When Beowulf protested that it was too much, Hrothgar laughed, and said he didn't think all the wealth in the world could repay what the Danes owed to him.

When the last of the gifts had been given and the last of the grateful speeches made Beowulf and his men were carried down the hill to Heorot and toasted yet again as the heroes of Denmark. Poems and songs had been composed during the day in celebration and were now performed for the first, but by no means the last, time. The dancing and singing, eating and drinking went on until the early hours of the morning.

The party came to an end when there was surprisingly little of the food and drink left and everyone realised how tired they were. They all walked back up to the castle together: Geat and Dane, servant and master, thanes, poets, singers and cooks, and one old king who now felt twenty years younger. No-one was asked to stay behind this time, and no-one did. They all went to bed and slept more soundly, and more safely, than they'd slept for many years.

The next day Beowulf and his men returned to their boat, accompanied by Hrothgar, Wealtheow and almost all of the Danish king's court. The people were happy but the procession was a little subdued. Some were sad to be saying goodbye to friends, all were saddened by the body of Ghorat which was given pride of place in the boat the grateful Danes had given the Geats. They set off for home escorted by dozens of smaller Danish boats to see them safely off.

That day marked the beginning of another journey. Over the years that followed, the stories of Beowulf, the slightly unlikely, slightly stocky, short sighted hero, travelled far and wide to every part of the world the Danes visited. Wherever the Danes travelled, Beowulf's fame travelled too.

Beowulf himself returned home to another hero's welcome from his own king Hygelac. When he tried to present Hygelac with the gifts he'd been given by the Danes the king wouldn't hear of it. "They're yours," he said as he hugged Beowulf yet again. "You have earned, and you deserve, everything you have."

"But I'm in your service, sire," Beowulf pointed out, "and all I have therefore belongs to you."

"If all I ever have from you is the wisdom and loyalty you've always shown me, and the courage and skill you lent to the Danes, then I can ask for nothing more," Hygelac said.

And Beowulf was loyal to Hygelac right up to their last battle together when, after Hygelac's death and the defeat of the Geats, Beowulf had to swim home across an icy cold sea in full armour.

On his return to Gotland he was invited to be king. His modesty made him refuse at first, but eventually he accepted the throne and it's said that he ruled the Geats with wisdom, kindness and courage for as long as fifty years.

And as for the Danes, they slept peacefully every night after Beowulf returned home. No more monsters came roaming through the forests, no more blood was spilt by sharp teeth and strong claws. In killing the mother Beowulf had killed the last of the family, and the Danes were finally safe.

Unless, of course, there are others.... still sleeping.

John Harris is a professional storyteller and writer who works exclusively with children and young people, visiting schools and libraries across the UK and Ireland. For more information please visit:

www.johnharristhestoryteller.com